Printed and Published in Great Britain by D. C. THOMSON & CO., LTD., 185 Fleet Street, London EC4A 2HS.
© D. C. THOMSON & CO., LTD., 1999. **ISBN** 0-85116-703-9

WHAT ARE YOU DOING FOR 2000?

A carrot for your nose,
Mr Snowman — you're finished!

Wonder how Mo's snowman
would like a snowball!

Argh! The snowman's got
its very own force field.

Chuckle!

CRAZY DAISY

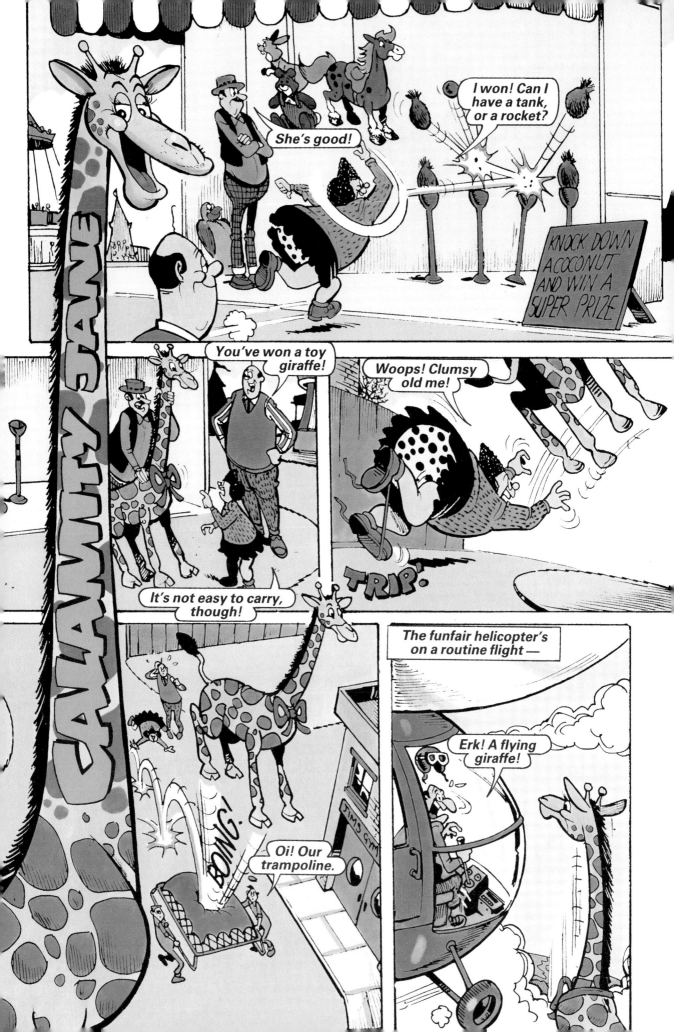

TALES FROM NEW HAMSTERDAM

"In case you don't know it, the name's Hamster, Mike Hamster, Private Eye. Under the street, in the pipes, tunnels and sewers, is the City of New Hamsterdam. Sure, it stinks but I love it. It's my kinda town."

"I was on a case when I first got scent of trouble brewing."

First holiday in years an' I can't get the case shut . . . Sniff . . . I know that smell.

"It was my informant, Squeaky Clean. At least the squeaky part was right."

Mr Hamster, word in the pipes is the Fromaggio Mob is up to somethin' big.

"Boss Fromaggio was a real ratfink. Him an' his goons were responsible for half the crimes in the city."

They're holdin' a secret meetin' at this address. It's a downtown squeakeasy.

"The holiday would have to wait."

You'd better take these and get outta town.

I'm gone. The Fromaggios don't like anybody rattin' on 'em.

"Bustin' this mob would be my ticket to the big time. There was no time to lose so I hopped a taxi."

Downtown an' quick.

It's a messy one. The Fromaggio Mob are history.

"It was a mess, all right."

Eggs?

Yeah. An' I want 'em stopped before there's any more foul play.

"Fowl play was more like it, as we were soon to discover. News of the mob's sticky end was out on the streets."

Read all about it!

ST VALENTINE'S DAY MOUSEACRE

as too late.
place was
rmin' with
s when I
ved."

EASY CHEESY'S
LIMBURGER
BAR

Hamster!

POLICE POLICE POLICE

News travels
fast.

What's the
story, O'Malley?

The whole lot, eggstinct.
Guess they won't be shelling
out for new suits.

This is no time
for bad yolks . . .
I mean jokes.

"It was Nibbles O'Malley,
my old pal in the Mice Squad."

Nobody from this
city would take
on the Fromaggios.

You mean an
outside gang are
muscling in?

PRESS

"Any wiseguy that tried to
take over soon left town."

Dis is Vinnie
da Vole's territory
now!

Oh,
yeah?

"Some went easily.
Others had to be
egged on."

I didn't see a thing.

This is getting out of control.

Yeah. It'll be a real feather in your cap if you catch these guys.

"Then I saw it."

Speaking of feathers . . . I think I've figured out where our guests are from.

"If the birds were invading, I needed to talk to a stool pigeon."

Give me the dirt on Al and you'll be in birdseed for life.

Coo. Deal!

"He sang like a canary."

The cops are closin' in on Al back home. He came here to lay low.

POLICE

"That night, the boat arrived. It was going like clockwork."

"The corn was supposed to be headed for the grain bank."

CORN

"Chick-ago. That city was for the birds."

Doo-be-doo-be-doo . . .

"Al Capon, with his moll, Rhode Island Red, ran the Chicken gang with a wing of iron."

"I had a plan but I needed O'Malley's help."

This had better work, Hamster. I don't want to end up with egg on my face.

"So my plan was hatched."

Eggsellent!

DAILY RODENT
MASSIVE CORN SHIPMENT EXPECTED

"I didn't reckon it was gonna make it."

Nice an' easy.

Freeze, rodents!

Hand over the corn or be egged out of eggsistence.

The Godfeather!

"That's when I dropped my bombshell."

Time's up, Capon!

Eh? Am I crackin' up

No. I am!

ZOOM!

HONEST RUTH

THERE WAS A GIRL CALLED HONEST RUTH,
WHO ONLY EVER TOLD THE TRUTH.
SHE TOLD A MAN HIS GREAT BIG NOSE,
ALMOST REACHED DOWN TO HIS TOES.
HER MOTHER'S CHIPS, YOUNG RUTH WOULD SAY,
WERE BAKED AS DRY AS STRAWS OF HAY.
ON SEEING HER SISTER'S PARTY DRESS,
SHE LAUGHED AND SHOUTED "WHAT A MESS!"
SHE TOLD HER BEST PAL THAT HER HAIR,
LOOKED LIKE STUFFING FROM A CHAIR.
SHE TOLD A LITTLE BOY CALLED RUSS,
HE HAD A FACE LIKE THE BACK OF A BUS.
"DAD," SHE SHOUTED NEXT, "YOUR SOCKS
LOOK LIKE THEY'VE CAUGHT THE CHICKENPOX!"

NEXT SHE PHONED HER UNCLE RICK,
TO SAY HIS SINGING MADE HER SICK.
SHE EVEN SAID THAT PRINCE, HER DOG,
HAD GREAT BIG EYES JUST LIKE A FROG.
FINALLY SHE SAID HER NEXT DOOR NEIGHBOUR,
SHOULD HAVE TO DO FIVE YEARS' HARD LABOUR.
SHE SAID, "THERE'S NO-ONE, DON'T YOU SEE,
IS PERFECT, 'CEPT FOR LITTLE ME."
ONE DAY OUR RUTH SHE CHANCED TO SEE,
A YOUNG CHAP KNOWN AS HONEST LEE.
WHO SAID, "OH, RUTH! YOUR TOOTH'S NOT STRAIGHT,
IT'S LIKE A CREAKY, SQUEAKY GATE!"
RUTH SCREAMED AND CRIED ABOUT HER TOOTH,
SHE DIDN'T LIKE THE HONEST TRUTH.

ADRIAN THE BARBARIAN

"I'm off to the shops. Remember to have your bath, Adrian."

"I will, Mum. 'Bye!"

"Rain! So much for the weatherman's forecast."

And soon —

"Funny — I'm running the bath, but my feet are getting wet already!"

"We're having a flood. That's why!"

"Abandon house! I'll use my bath as a boat!"

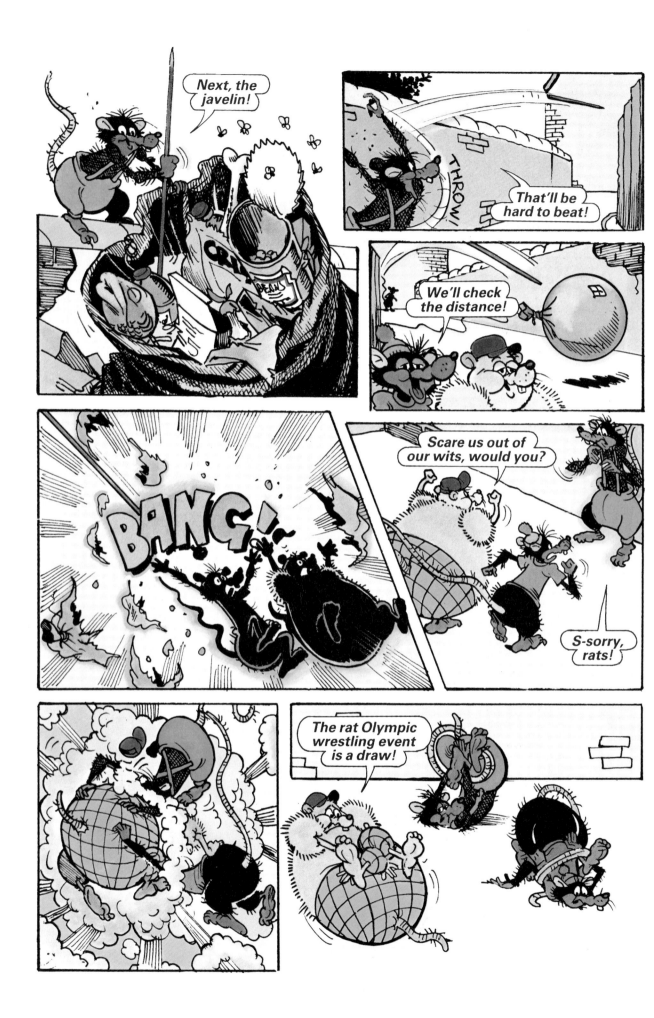

GINGER

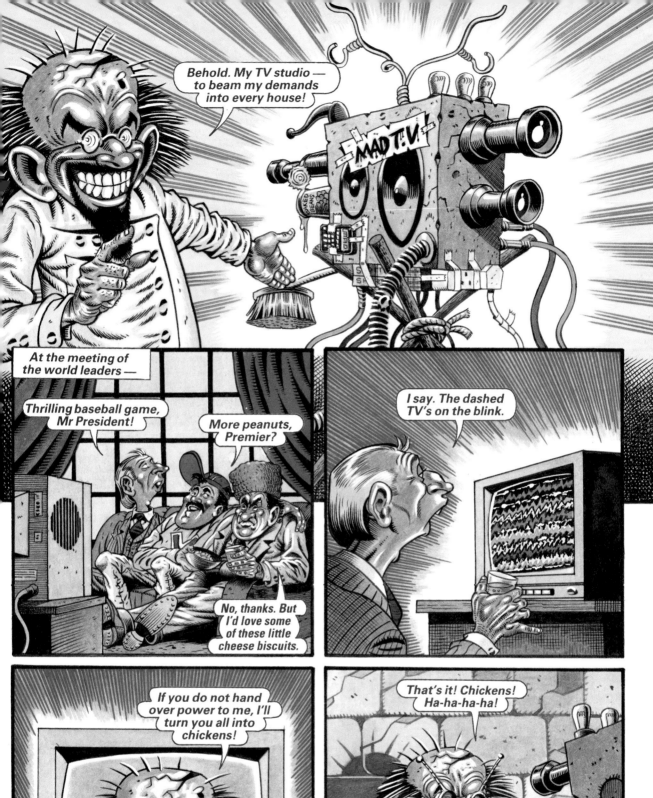

WHAT ARE YOU DOING FOR 2000?

About mi family an Ancestors by

WENDY WILHELMINA WEBSTER

witch and gold swimming medal winner – TROO !!!

illustrated by me

our coat of arms

GRATE, GRATE, GRATE, GRATE, GRATE grandma GRISELDA waz ahead of her time. She was the first in towne to swop her broome for a VACCUM CLEANER

She could go faster than all the other witches on it but was a pane in the neck emptyin the bag after every flite

Poor old GRATE, GRATE, UNCIE WOLFGANG invented a poshun to cure baldyness. usin' werewolf milk an' other stuff. He went all hairy an started barkin an drinkin out of the toylet bowl. He won Best of Bred at Crufts – thoe nobody knows what breed he waz

BEFORE   AFTER.

COLONEL LIVINGSTON BAGSHOT WEBSTER waz the wurst Explorer ever – He tried to find the Elehpants graveYard. the Sauce of the NILE an the Lost City of ATLANTIS but couldn't even find his socks so he stayed at home

He was thrown out of the FREEZER CENTRE tryin to find the ABOMINABLE SNOWMAN IN the FRIDGE

EBENEZER WEBSTER was so mean he wouldn't speak coz he didn't want to waste his words on everybody. He would put the candle out any time he blinked coz he didn't want to waste light he couldn't see. Every Christmas he went to live in the forest so he didn't have to buy a Christmas tree

merry xmas

£10.50 Please

Miserable ol' Ebenezer

LUCRETIA WEBSTER loved to cook huge meals an hold bankwets. Which is a pity coz she was a rotten cook. Her liver and grapefruit pancakes could reduce a grown man to tears, speshally if he dropped one on his foot.

Her onlie successful recipe was for scones and she sold thousands of them which were used as cobbles for the roads

GRATE GRATE GRANMA CLARISSA wa3 very vain and thort she wa2 the most lovely thing ever. She had a flying mirror that went everywhere in front of her. All her pashuns were used to make her more lovely, like Luscious Lipstick, magic Mascara an' enchanted eye liner

MAKE UP

DISASTER - her vanishin cream worked too well an she went invisable

MAKE UP

Mi MUM, DEAR OL' DAD An' (larst but not leest) ME.
Dear ol' dad works for a ball bearing company an' he says it keeps him rollin along. Mum cooks an cleans an does all sorts of stuff. She says she's a housewife, which is daft coz she's not married to the house. I reckon she's got the worst job in the world...lookin after me. Mi parents are not witches but I think they're MAGIC.

DAD

mum

me

SPORT ON TV

catapuss mi cat

HOW TO SPELL

GRIM FAIRY TALES

DREADTIME STORIES AND NURSERY CRIMES

Meet the Brothers Grim.

Are you sitting comfortably, kiddies?

Because you won't be. Snigger.

Little Bo Peep

~or~

The Silencer of the Lambs

"Little Bo Peep has lost her sheep . . ."

WANTED

"And doesn't know where to find them."

SHEEP RADAR

"At least, that's what the witnesses said . . ."

"And we can't ask Humpty 'cause he bashed in his head."

"But it was Little Boy Blue who caused the drop . . ."

"And he was arrested outside his omelette shop."

GORDON BLUE'S RESTAURANT

This month's special:—
omelette
also
egg + chips

Don't believe us, eh, kiddies?

Then feast your eyes on these!

Okay, chaps. Plan B!

Could somebody call a doctor?

And they lived unhappily ever after.

Christmas Carol

It's Christmas tomorrow, readers — and I can't wait!

I wish it could be Christmas every day!

Turkey every dinner time.

Except I'd eat so much turkey I'd turn into one!

BABY CROCKETT

Me's been at the garden centre wiv Dad!

Buying a tree!

First we have to dig a nice, deep hole for it.

Look at that, Baby. You're the same height as the tree!

So me is!

Me's gonna see if me can grow quicker than 'at tree!

Me's gonna water me's self.

GINGER

I've to check everything's taken care of before bed time!

Make sure the rabbit doesn't get a draught.

HOME SWEET HOME

Keep the frost off Mum's flowers.

CLUNK!

Make sure the gate's closed, and that's it!

Did you de-activate the destructo-robot in our garage?

MUM

CHOC